Bible Quizzes
for Church Newsletters 2

Bible Quizzes for Church Newsletters 2

Frank R. Hoffman

BAKER BOOK HOUSE
Grand Rapids, Michigan 49516

Copyright © 1989 by Baker Books
a division of Baker Book House Company
P.O. Box 6287, Grand Rapids, MI 49516-6287

ISBN: 0-8010-4342-5

Third printing, February 1994

Printed in the United States of America

Contents

For Marion

Animals and Birds

Although the Bible mentions many animals and birds, it isn't always clear exactly which animal is intended. Translators differ in this matter. Can you identify the animals mentioned in the verses below?

1. "It is easier for a _____ to go through the eye of a needle."
2. "Flee from the midst of Babylon, and go out of the land of Chaldeans, and be as _____ before the flock."
3. "I am . . . like an _____ of the waste places."
4. "Many _____ encompass me, strong _____ of Bashan surround me."
5. "I clothed thee also with broidered work, and shod thee with _____ skin."
6. "He [Samson] turned aside to see the carcase of the _____."
7. "Once every three years the fleet ships of Tarshish used to come bringing gold, silver, ivory, _____, and _____."
8. "You know that your father and his men are mighty men, and that they are enraged, like a _____ robbed of her _____."
9. "The young _____ roar for their prey, seeking their food from God."
10. "I am like a _____ of the wilderness."

Answers

1. camel, Matthew 19:24, KJV
2. he-goats, Jeremiah 50:8
3. owl, Psalm 102:6
4. bulls, Psalm 22:12–13
5. badgers', Ezekiel 16:10, KJV
6. lion, Judges 14:8, KJV
7. apes/peacocks, 1 Kings 10:22
8. bear/cubs, 2 Samuel 17:8
9. lions, Psalm 104:21
10. pelican, Psalm 102:6, KJV

Arms and Armor

Many offensive and defensive weapons are mentioned in the Bible. Can you identify them?

1. David used it to kill the giant Goliath.
2. David used it to cut off Goliath's head.
3. Saul tried to hit David with one.
4. David ordered that men of Judah be taught its use.
5. A man who bears false witness is like this weapon.
6. They were destroyed in the Red Sea.
7. Solomon had 300 of these made from beaten gold.
8. Saul gave one of brass to David when he met Goliath.
9. Isaiah and Ephesians mention putting this on.
10. Those Goliath wore were made of bronze.

a. maul
b. shields
c. sword
d. greaves
e. breastplate
f. bow
g. sling
h. chariots
i. spear
j. helmet

Answers

1. g, 1 Samuel 17:40
2. c, 1 Samuel 17:51
3. i, 1 Samuel 18:11
4. f, 2 Samuel 1:18
5. a, Proverbs 25:18
6. h, Exodus 15:4
7. b, 1 Kings 10:17
8. j, 1 Samuel 17:38
9. e, Isaiah 59:17; Ephesians 6:14
10. d, 1 Samuel 17:6

Body-Building

God created man and woman. Try your hand at "creating" the human form by supplying the missing words in the verses given below.

1. Jesus said, "And do not swear by your _____."
2. Job was asked, "Have you an _____ like God?"
3. Paul cried out, "I bear on my _____ the marks of Jesus."
4. Isaiah urged, "Take the millstones and grind meal, put off your veil, strip off your robe, uncover your _____."
5. Quoting Isaiah, Paul spoke and said, "How beautiful on the mountain are the _____ of those who bring good news."
6. The proverb tells us, "Keep my commandments and live, keep my teachings as the apple of your eye, bind them on your _____."
7. Still another proverbs says, "Let not loyalty and faithfulness forsake you; bind them about your _____."
8. Moses warned, "Beware lest you say in your heart, 'My power and the might of my _____ have gotten me this wealth.'"
9. When Joseph was commissioned by Pharaoh, "they cried before him, 'Bow the _____.'"

Answers

1. head, Matthew 5:36
2. arm, Job 40:9
3. body, Galatians 6:17
4. legs, Isaiah 47:2
5. feet, Isaiah 52:7, NIV
6. fingers, Proverbs 7:2–3
7. neck, Proverbs 3:3
8. hand, Deuteronomy 8:17
9. knee, Genesis 41:43

What Did They Buy?

Most of the purchases recorded in the Bible were for land or food. But there are other purchases recorded. Can you tell what is being bought by supplying the missing word(s) below?

1. David bought a _____ _____ to build an altar to stop a plague.
2. Omri bought a _____ on which to build a city.
3. "Buy the _____, and sell it not" (KJV).
4. "That we may buy the _____ for silver, . . ."
5. " . . . and the _____ for a pair of sandals."
6. "Come, buy _____ and _____ without money and without price."
7. A man sold everything to get money to buy a _____.
8. A merchant sold everything to get money to buy a _____.
9. Five women missed a wedding party because they had gone to buy _____.
10. Three women bought _____ to anoint the body of Jesus.

Answers

1. threshing floor, 2 Samuel 24:21
2. hill, 1 Kings 16:24
3. truth, Proverbs 23:23
4. poor, Amos 8:6
5. needy, Amos 8:6
6. wine/milk, Isaiah 55:1
7. field, Matthew 13:44
8. pearl, Matthew 13:45–46
9. oil, Matthew 25:10
10. spices, Mark 16:1

Chapter and Verse

Some passages of the Bible are considered so important and meaningful that many people know them by chapter and verse. Do you? Match the two columns and see how well you do.

1. The Ten Commandments
2. The Birth of Jesus
3. The Lord's Prayer
4. The Sermon on the Mount
5. The Great Commandments
6. The Parable of the Prodigal Son
7. The Parable of the Good Samaritan
8. The "Golden Rule"
9. The "Love" Chapter
10. The Gospel Condensed

a. Matthew 6:9–15
b. Luke 15:11–32
c. 1 Corinthians 13
d. Exodus 20
e. Matthew 7:12
f. Luke 10:30–37
g. Luke 2:8–14
h. Matthew 22:34–40
i. John 3:16
j. Matthew 5, 6, 7

Answers

1. d
2. g
3. a
4. j
5. h

6. b
7. f
8. e
9. c
10. i

Children

Children are important in the Bible. They were, for example, special to Jesus, whose actions and teachings frequently focused on children. Here are some verses about children. Can you supply the missing word(s)?

1. It was said of Moses, "he was a _____ child."
2. Before God, Jeremiah pleaded, "I cannot _____ for I am a child."
3. The psalmist said, "Out of the mouths of babes . . . hast thou ordained _____."
4. The proverb recommends: "_____ up a child in the way he should go."
5. Isaiah mentions animals and says, "a little child shall _____ them."
6. Jesus said, "See that you do not _____ one of these little ones."
7. Jesus said, "It is not the will of my Father . . . that one of these little ones should _____."
8. Children were brought to Jesus that "he might lay his hands on them and _____."
9. Paul said, "We were gentle among you, like a _____ taking care of her children."
10. Paul reminds Timothy, "And that from a child thou hast known the _____ _____."

Answers

1. goodly, Exodus 2:2
2. speak, Jeremiah 1:6, KJV
3. strength, Psalm 8:2, KJV
4. train, Proverbs 22:6
5. lead, Isaiah 11:6
6. despise, Matthew 18:10
7. perish, Matthew 18:14
8. pray, Matthew 19:13
9. nurse, 1 Thessalonians 2:7
10. holy scriptures, 2 Timothy 3:15, KJV

Do You Know This Church?

There are seven churches mentioned in the early chapters of the Book of Revelation. Can you identify the church being referred to by its special characterization, and by supplying the missing word?

1. The "compromising" church was led by a woman called _____.
2. The "missionary" church bore the name of a _____ church.
3. The "passionless" church abandoned its first _____.
4. The "tolerant" church is in a city that houses "_____ throne."
5. The "arrogant" church had need of _____.
6. The "persecuted" church will not suffer "the _____ death."
7. The "dead" church had "the name of being _____."

Answers

1. Jezebel/Thyatira, Revelation 2:20
2. faithful/Philadelphia, Revelation 3:7–13, LB
3. love/Ephesus, Revelation 2:1–7
4. Satan's/Pergamum, Revelation 2:12–17
5. nothing/Laodicea, Revelation 3:14–22
6. second/Smyrna, Revelation 2:8–11
7. alive/Sardis, Revelation 3:1–6

Clothing and Fabrics

With the exception of the very wealthy, most people in biblical times wore clothes that were quite practical. Some articles of clothing are mentioned in Scripture. Can you identify the fabrics and items of dress from the following descriptions?

1. John the Baptist's clothes were made of _____ hair.
2. John also wore a leather _____.
3. Pharaoh gave Joseph his signet ring and dressed him in fine _____.
4. Rahab hid men under stalks of _____.
5. Jesus had a seamless _____, woven from top to bottom.
6. Samuel, as a child, ministered before the Lord in a linen _____.
7. The good wife in Proverbs seeks _____ and flax to work with.
8. At the "burning bush," God told Moses to take off his _____.
9. Miraculous powers were attached to Paul's _____ or _____.
10. Paul asked Timothy to bring his _____, books, and parchments.

Answers

1. camel's, Matthew 3:4
2. girdle, Matthew 3:4
3. linen, Genesis 41:42
4. flax, Joshua 2:1–6
5. tunic, John 19:23
6. ephod, 1 Samuel 2:18
7. wool, Proverbs 31:13
8. shoes, Exodus 3:5
9. handkerchiefs/aprons, Acts 19:12
10. cloak, 2 Timothy 4:13

For Your Comfort

God ministers to us in our deepest hurts and hardest trials. Isaiah heard it: "Comfort ye, comfort ye, my people, saith your God" (Isa. 40:1, KJV). Can you supply the missing word(s) in these verses that speak so eloquently of God's comfort?

1. "Blessed are they that _____, for they shall be comforted."
2. "Thy _____ and thy _____, they comfort me."
3. "Sing, O heavens; and be joyful, O earth; and break forth into singing, O _____: for the LORD hath comforted his people. . . ."
4. "For the LORD shall comfort _____: he will comfort all her waste places. . . ."
5. "As one whom his _____ comforts, so will I comfort you. . . ."
6. (Jesus) said, "Daughter, be of good comfort; thy _____ hath made thee whole."
7. "So the church . . . was built up; and walking in the fear of the Lord and in the comfort of the _____ _____ it was multiplied."
8. "Blessed be the God and Father of our Lord Jesus Christ, the Father of _____ and God of all comfort. . . ."
9. "But God, who comforts the _____, comforted us by the coming of Titus. . . ."

Answers

1. mourn, Matthew 5:4, KJV
2. rod/staff, Psalm 23:4, KJV
3. mountains, Isaiah 49:13, KJV
4. Zion, Isaiah 51:3, KJV
5. mother, Isaiah 66:13
6. faith, Matthew 9:22, KJV
7. Holy Spirit, Acts 9:31
8. mercies, 2 Corinthians 1:3
9. downcast, 2 Corinthians 7:6

Lord of the Dance

A contemporary hymn reminds us that Jesus is "Lord of the Dance." Can you supply the missing word(s) in the following verses about dancing?

1. _____ was angry when he saw the calf and the dancing.
2. "Then _____ came to his home . . . and his daughter came out to meet him with timbrels and with dances."
3. "The women came . . . singing and dancing to meet _____."
4. "_____ danced before the Lord."
5. "A time to _____, and a time to dance."
6. "There ostriches will dwell, and there _____ will dance."
7. "We _____ to you, and you did not dance."
8. "For when _____ daughter came in and danced, she pleased Herod and his guests."
9. "Thou hast turned for me my _____ into dancing."
10. Benjamites were to watch "if the daughters of _____ come out to dance in the dances."

Answers

1. Moses, Exodus 32:19
2. Jephthah, Judges 11:34
3. King Saul, 1 Samuel 18:6
4. David, 2 Samuel 6:14
5. mourn, Ecclesiastes 3:4
6. satyrs, Isaiah 13:21
7. piped, Matthew 11:17
8. Herodias', Mark 6:22
9. mourning, Psalm 30:11
10. Shiloh, Judges 21:20

David

How well do you remember Old Testament stories? Try this quiz on the life of David, the shepherd boy who grew up to become Israel's greatest king.

1. David's first great deed was to slay which Philistine giant?
2. David's arch enemy was king _____.
3. _____ was David's most beloved friend.
4. A cave called _____ was David's hiding place.
5. David was anointed king of Judah at _____.
6. David's treacherous, rebellious son was _____.
7. David made an alliance with _____, king of Tyre.
8. David offered kindness to a lame man, _____.
9. The prophet _____ confronted David with his sin.
10. David's brilliant son and heir was _____.

Answers

1. Goliath, 1 Samuel 17:23
2. Saul, 1 Samuel 18:29
3. Jonathan, 1 Samuel 18:3
4. Adullam, 1 Samuel 22:1
5. Hebron, 2 Samuel 2:3
6. Absalom, 2 Samuel 15:1–6
7. Hiram, 2 Samuel 5:11
8. Mephibosheth, 2 Samuel 9:6
9. Nathan, 2 Samuel 12:7
10. Solomon, 1 Kings 2:1

12

We’re Family

The church has always believed that God established the family as the basic unit of society. “We’re family” is a statement of justifiable pride, if it’s an expression of love. Can you identify the relative (second column) of the person in the first column, and the relationship between the two (third column).

1. Miriam
2. Abimelech
3. Lois
4. John (the Baptist)
5. Benjamin
6. Abraham
7. Esau
8. Ruth
9. Martha
10. Laban

a. Jesus
b. Lazarus
c. Joseph
d. Aaron
e. Timothy
f. Rachel
g. Naomi
h. Jacob
i. Jotham
j. Lot

k. Brothers
l. Cousins
m. Father and daughter
n. Sister and brother
o. Brothers
p. Uncle/nephew
q. Twin brothers
r. Mother/daughter-in-law
s. Grandmother/grandson

Answers

1. d/n, Exodus 15:20
2. i/o, Judges 9:5
3. e/s, 2 Timothy 1:5
4. a/l, Luke 1:36
5. c/k, Genesis 42:4
6. j/p, Genesis 11:31
7. h/q, Genesis 25:24–26
8. g/r, Ruth 1:1–5
9. b/n, John 11:1–4
10. f/m, Genesis 29:10

Fasting

Fasting was in both Old and New Testaments. Jesus drew a distinction between true and false fasting (Matt. 6:16–18). Can you complete these sentences?

1. Israel fasted before battling "the children of" _____.
2. Saul ordered fasting before battle with the _____.
3. Valiant men fasted seven days after burying _____.
4. David and his men fasted for his friend _____.
5. Ahab fasted when confronted with his sin by _____.
6. Learning the remnant suffered, a fast was held by _____.
7. Esther wanted to call the Jews to fast through _____.
8. Fasting forty days in the wilderness was _____.
9. Cornelius fasted before sending for _____.
10. A fast was held before choosing Saul and _____.

a. Mordecai
b. Jonathan
c. Jesus
d. Philistines
e. Nehemiah
f. Barnabas
g. Benjamin
h. Elijah
i. Saul
j. Peter

Answers

1. g, Judges 20:25
2. d, 1 Samuel 14:24
3. i, 1 Samuel 31:13
4. b, 2 Samuel 1:11–12
5. h, 1 Kings 21:17–27
6. e, Nehemiah 1:4
7. a, Esther 4:15–16
8. c, Matthew 4:1–2
9. j, Acts 10:30–32, KJV
10. f, Acts 13:1–2

Fathers

Jesus taught us to call God "Father" (Matt. 6:7). So God is the one who defines for us what is true fatherhood. Below are the names of some fathers (left-hand column) and sons (right-hand column). Can you match them?

1. Zechariah	a. Rehoboam
2. David	b. Cain
3. Abraham	c. Lot
4. Adam	d. Solomon
5. Jesse	e. David
6. Elkanah	f. John (the Baptist)
7. Joash	g. Gideon
8. Solomon	h. Isaac
9. Noah	i. Samuel
10. Haran	j. Shem, Ham, and Japheth

Answers

1. f, Luke 1:57–63
2. d, 1 Kings 2:12
3. h, Genesis 21:2–5
4. b, Genesis 4:1
5. e, 1 Samuel 17:12–14
6. i, 1 Samuel 1:1
7. g, Judges 6:29
8. a, 1 Kings 14:21
9. j, Genesis 6:10
10. c, Genesis 11:27

What's in the Field?

Fields are abundant in Palestine, and often mentioned in the Bible. Frequently a field has something very important in it. Can you tell what is in the field by supplying the missing word?

1. "And he [Jacob] looked, and behold a _____ in the field. . . ."
2. "In the _____ that is in the field of Machpelah . . . which Abraham bought. . . ."
3. David's soldiers "found an _____ in the field" (near Besor).
4. A son of the prophets "went out into the field to gather _____, and found a wild vine. . . ."
5. "_____ springeth up as hemlock in the furrows of the field."
6. "And there were in the same country _____ abiding in the field. . . ."
7. "I charge you, O ye daughters of Jerusalem, by the roes, and by the _____ of the field. . . ."
8. "Consider the _____ of the field."
9. "The kingdom of heaven is like a _____ hidden in a field."
10. (Jesus) "went through the _____ fields on the sabbath day."

Answers

1. well, Genesis 29:1–2
2. cave, Genesis 49:30
3. Egyptian, 1 Samuel 30:11
4. herbs, 2 Kings 4:39
5. judgment, Hosea 10:4
6. shepherds, Luke 2:8
7. hinds, Song of Solomon 2:7
8. lilies, Matthew 6:28
9. treasure, Matthew 13:44
10. corn, Mark 2:23

Some Firsts

Here are some Bible firsts. All of them have a New Testament reference. Can you supply the name or phrase?

1. Who was the first person to call Jesus "Lord"?
2. In which town did Jesus perform his first miracle?
3. In which city were the disciples first called Christians?
4. Who was the first Christian martyr?
5. Who were the first Christian missionaries?
6. Who was the first Gentile convert?
7. In which city was the first Christian church located?
8. Which is the first commandment in importance?
9. Who was the first disciple to recognize Jesus as the Christ?
10. Which is the first commandment with a promise?

Answers

1. Elizabeth, Luke 1:43
2. Cana, John 2:1–11
3. Antioch, Acts 11:26
4. Stephen, Acts 7:54–60
5. Paul and Barnabas, Galatians 2:9
6. Cornelius, Acts 10
7. Jerusalem, Acts 2:5, 41–47
8. to love God, Mark 12:29–30
9. Peter, Matthew 16:16
10. Honor your father and mother, Ephesians 6:2

Don't Be Foolish

"The fool hath said in his heart, There is no God" (Ps. 14:1, KJV). Perhaps that's why fools fare so badly in the Bible, especially in the Book of Proverbs. Can you supply the missing word(s) in the following quotations from the King James Version?

1. "The fear of the LORD is the beginning of knowledge: but fools despise _____ and _____."
2. "The lips of the righteous feed many: but fools die for want of _____."
3. "A fool despiseth his father's instruction: but he that regardeth reproof is _____."
4. "Understanding is a well-spring of life unto him that hath it: but the instruction of fools is _____."
5. "A fool's _____ enter into contention. . . ."
6. "A fool's mouth is his _____, and his lips are the snare of his soul."
7. A foolish son is a _____ to his father, and bitterness to her that bare him."
8. "Seest thou a man wise in his own _____? there is more hope of a fool than of him."
9. "The legs of the lame are not equal: so is a _____ in the mouth of fools."
10. "The great God that formed all things both _____ the fool, and _____ transgressors."

Answers

1. wisdom/instruction, Proverbs 1:7
2. sense, Proverbs 10:21
3. prudent, Proverbs 15:5
4. folly, Proverbs 16:22
5. lips, Proverbs 18:6
6. destruction, Proverbs 18:7
7. grief, Proverbs 17:25
8. conceit, Proverbs 26:12
9. parable, Proverbs 26:7
10. rewardeth/rewardeth, Proverbs 26:10

Friends

Deuteronomy describes a friend as a person "who is as your own soul" (13:6). Having a true friend is one of life's most beautiful experiences. But the depth and significance of a friendship depends on the people involved. Identify the "friends" in the verses below.

1. Who spoke to Moses face to face, "as a man speaks to his friend"?
2. He was David's closest and most beloved friend.
3. What were the names of Job's three "friends"?
4. He was described as a "friend of sinners."
5. Jesus said this friend was asleep.
6. Pilate was accused of not being a friend to whom?
7. Who did Herod become friendly with during Jesus' trial?
8. Which centurion gathered his close friends for a meeting with Peter?
9. Which Old Testament patriarch did James describe as "a friend of God"?
10. Who said the greatest love is to "lay down one's life for one's friends"?

Answers

1. God, Exodus 33:11
2. Jonathan, 1 Samuel 18:1
3. Eliphaz, Bildad, and Zophar, Job 2:11
4. Jesus, Matthew 9:11; Luke 7:34
5. Lazarus, John 11:11
6. Caesar, John 19:12
7. Pilate, Luke 23:12
8. Cornelius, Acts 10:24
9. Abraham, James 2:23
10. Jesus, John 15:13

God's Fullness

The following verses have the word *full* in common. By supplying the missing word, can you identify what this fullness consists of?

1. The psalmist proclaims that "the voice of the LORD is powerful, the voice of the LORD is full of _____."
2. The psalmist says, "Happy is the man who has his quiver full of them." What? _____.
3. Isaiah heard seraphim saying of God, "The whole earth is full of his _____."
4. Isaiah sees a day when "the earth shall be full of the _____ of the LORD, as the waters cover the sea."
5. God's law is concerned that we give "a full and _____ weight."
6. Malachi says, "Bring the full _____ into the storehouse."
7. John says, "The Word . . . dwelt among us, full of grace and _____."
8. Jesus said, "Ask, and you will receive, that your _____ may be full."
9. The church was to choose seven (deacons), "full of the Spirit and of _____."
10. Stephen was said to be "full of _____ and of the Holy Spirit."

Answers

1. majesty, Psalm 29:4
2. arrows/children, Psalm 127:4–5
3. glory, Isaiah 6:3
4. knowledge, Isaiah 11:9
5. just, Deuteronomy 25:15
6. tithes, Malachi 3:10
7. truth, John 1:14
8. joy, John 16:24
9. wisdom, Acts 6:3
10. faith, Acts 6:5

What's Gone Is Gone!

"What's gone is gone!" Sometimes, but not always. Supply the missing word(s) in the following verses and you'll see that sometimes what's gone is gone, but sometimes only temporarily gone.

1. "All we like _____ have gone astray."
2. "He perceived that _____ had gone out of him."
3. It was said of Jesus that "the _____ is gone after him."
4. "For the _____ passes over it, and it is gone."
5. "For lo, the winter is past, the _____ is over and gone."
6. "When the _____ _____ is gone out of a man, he passes through waterless places seeking rest, but he finds none."
7. "Give us some of your _____, for our lamps are going out."
8. "As a man burns up _____ until it is all gone."
9. "I am gone like a shadow at _____; I am shaken off like a locust."

Answers

1. sheep, Isaiah 53:6
2. virtue, Mark 5:30, KJV
3. world, John 12:19, KJV
4. wind, Psalm 103:16
5. rain, Song of Solomon 2:11
6. unclean spirit, Matthew 12:43
7. oil, Matthew 25:8, KJV
8. dung, 1 Kings 14:10, KJV
9. evening, Psalm 109:23

Heaven

Jesus said, "Because I live, you will live also" (John 14:19). Heaven is the name the Bible gives to this place where we will live with him. Can you supply the missing word in the following verses about heaven?

1. "Lay up for yourselves _____ in heaven."
2. "I saw _____ fall like lightning from heaven."
3. "Rejoice that your names are _____ in heaven."
4. "Was the _____ of John from heaven or from men?"
5. "I saw the _____ descend as a dove from heaven."
6. "I am the _____ which came down from heaven."
7. "Do not _____, either by heaven or by earth."
8. "I saw the . . . new _____, coming down out of heaven from God."
9. "I know a man in Christ who . . . was caught up to the _____ heaven."
10. "I heard . . . the loud voice of a great multitude in heaven, crying, '_____!'"

Answers

1. treasures, Matthew 6:20
2. Satan, Luke 10:18
3. written, Luke 10:20
4. baptism, Luke 20:4
5. Spirit, John 1:32
6. bread, John 6:41
7. swear, James 5:12
8. Jerusalem, Revelation 21:2
9. third, 2 Corinthians 12:2
10. Hallelujah, Revelation 19:1

He Is Able

On the basis of their astonishing experience, the early Christians knew the risen Christ was able to do all things in them and through them. What things? Supply the missing word(s) to find out, using the King James Version.

1. "He is able to _____ them that are tempted."
2. "He is able also to _____ them . . . that come unto God by him. . . ."
3. He is able "to _____ you from falling."
4. "He is able even to _____ all things unto himself."
5. "He is able to _____ that which I have committed unto him against that day."
6. "No man in heaven . . . was able to open the _____."
7. He "is able to do _____ _____ above all that we ask or think."

Answers

1. succor, Hebrews 2:18
2. save, Hebrews 7:25
3. keep, Jude 24
4. subdue, Philippians 3:21
5. keep, 2 Timothy 1:12
6. book, Revelation 5:3
7. exceeding abundantly, Ephesians 3:20

Herbs, Plants, and Spices

The Bible mentions herbs, plants, and spices and also uses these items as symbols of human feeling—joy or sorrow. Can you identify the herbs, plants, and spices mentioned in the following verses?

1. "Consider the _____ of the field, how they grow . . . even Solomon in all his glory was not arrayed like one of these."
2. "From the _____ tree learn its lesson, as soon as its branch becomes tender and puts forth its leaves, you know that summer is near."
3. "Are _____ gathered from thorns, or figs from thistles?"
4. "Pomegranate, palm, and _____, all the trees of the field are withered."
5. "I am the _____ of Sharon, and the lily of the valleys."
6. "Spikenard and _____; calamus and cinnamon, with all trees of frankincense; myrrh and aloes, with all the chief spices."
7. "And the LORD said to Moses, 'Take sweet spices, stacte, and onycha, and _____, these sweet spices with pure frankincense. . . .'"
8. "We remember the fish, which we did eat in Egypt freely; the cucumbers and the melons, and the leeks, and the onions, and the _____."

Answers

1. lilies, Matthew 6:28–29
2. fig, Matthew 24:32
3. grapes, Matthew 7:16
4. apple, Joel 1:12
5. rose, Song of Solomon 2:1
6. saffron, Song of Solomon 4:14, KJV
7. galbanum, Exodus 30:34
8. garlick, Numbers 11:5, KJV

Hymns

Some of the greatest hymns of the church are based on verses of Scripture. Can you match the author and the hymn, and identify the passage?

1. God the Lord, a King Remaineth
2. Hark, the Herald Angels Sing
3. A Mighty Fortress Is Our God
4. Lead Kindly Light
5. Jesus Savior, Pilot Me
6. O God, Our Help in Ages Past
7. Ride on, Ride on in Majesty
8. In the Cross of Christ I Glory
9. Breathe on Me, Breath of God
10. O Little Town of Bethlehem

a. Martin Luther
b. John Bowring
c. Edward Hopper
d. Edwin Hatch
e. Isaac Watts
f. Henry Milman
g. John Wesley
h. Phillips Brooks
i. John Henry Newman
j. John Keble

Answers

1. j, Psalm 93
2. g, Luke 2:8–14
3. a, Psalm 46
4. i, Exodus 13:21–22
5. c, Matthew 8:23–27
6. e, Psalm 90
7. f, Matthew 21:1–11
8. b, Galatians 6:14
9. d, John 20:22
10. h, Luke 2:4

Idols

Both Old and New Testaments mention numerous gods and goddesses who were the objects of idolatrous worship. Can you identify them from the descriptions given below? References are to the King James Version.

1. She was the Phoenician (Zidonian) goddess of love.
2. Barnabas was likened to this Greek god.
3. He was the supreme god of the Amorites.
4. He was the god of the children of Ammon.
5. This moon goddess had a temple at Ephesus.
6. Forest deities of the Greeks and Romans.
7. He was a fire god worshiped by the Ammonites.
8. A Babylonian deity, he was god of vegetation.
9. Paul was likened to this Greek god.
10. He was a god of the Moabites.

a. Baal
b. Tammuz
c. Chemosh
d. Mercurius
e. Diana
f. Jupiter
g. Molech
h. Satyrs
i. Milcom
j. Ashtoreth

Answers

1. j, 1 Kings 11:5, 33
2. f, Acts 14:12
3. a, 1 Kings 16:32
4. i, 1 Kings 11:5, 33
5. e, Acts 19:27
6. h, Isaiah 13:21
7. g, 1 Kings 11:7
8. b, Ezekiel 8:14
9. d, Acts 14:12
10. c, 1 Kings 11:7

Increase

To increase something is to add to its substance, bulk, or volume, usually (but not always) in a positive sense. Supply the missing word to discover who or what is being increased in the verses cited below.

1. "When goods increase, they increase who _____ them."
2. "Of the increase of his _____ and of peace there shall be no end."
3. "He who increases knowledge, increases _____."
4. "And _____ increased in wisdom and in stature, and in favor with God and man."
5. "But [at Damascus] _____ increased all the more in strength."
6. Luke tells us in Acts: "The _____ . . . increased in number daily."
7. _____ said, "He must increase, but I must decrease."
8. The _____ pleaded, "Lord, increase our faith."
9. "Pleasant speech increases _____."
10. "And to him who has no might he increases _____."

Answers

1. eat, Ecclesiastes 5:11
2. government, Isaiah 9:7
3. sorrow, Ecclesiastes 1:18
4. Jesus, Luke 2:52
5. Saul, Acts 9:22
6. churches, Acts 16:5
7. John (the Baptist), John 3:30
8. disciples, Luke 17:5
9. persuasiveness, Proverbs 16:21
10. strength, Isaiah 40:29

Islands

Many islands dot the beautiful Mediterranean Sea. Some are mentioned in the Bible. Try your hand at matching the islands to the descriptions given below.

1. Ezekiel says men from this island were oarsmen.
2. Paul took refuge on this island during a storm.
3. Paul sailed close to this island before taking refuge.
4. Paul was shipwrecked on this island.
5. John was exiled on this island.
6. When Paul left Ephesus, he sailed first to this island.
7. The next day he sailed on to this island.
8. Paul sailed from Mitylene to this island.
9. God says (in Jeremiah) to cross to this island's coasts.
10. Although it is not named in the Bible, Paul stayed in the capital city of this island—Syracuse.

a. Patmos
b. Chios (Kios)
c. Rhodes
d. Cyprus (Chittim/ Kittim)
e. Cauda (Clauda)
f. Arvad
g. Cos (Coos)
h. Crete
i. Sicily
j. Malta (Melita)

Answers

1. f, Ezekiel 27:8, 11
2. e, Acts 27:16
3. h, Acts 27:13
4. j, Acts 28:1
5. a, Revelation 1:9

6. g, Acts 21:1
7. c, Acts 21:1
8. b, Acts 20:14–15
9. d, Jeremiah 2:10
10. i, Acts 28:12

Kings

Many kings are mentioned in the Bible; some malevolent, some benevolent. Only one is "King of kings" (Rev. 17:14). Can you match the kings with the descriptive phrase about them?

1. He was the first to rule Israel.
2. He danced before the ark of the covenant.
3. He rebuilt God's house in Judah at God's command.
4. He made Esther his queen.
5. He died the year Isaiah had his vision of the Lord.
6. He put Shadrach, Meshach, and Abednego in a furnace.
7. He put Daniel in the lion's den.
8. He was king when Jesus was born in Bethlehem.
9. He presided at Paul's trial at Caesarea.
10. He is King of kings, and Lord of lords.

a. Uzziah
b. Darius
c. Christ Jesus
d. David
e. Cyrus
f. Saul
g. Agrippa
h. Ahasuerus
i. Nebuchadnezzar
j. Herod

Answers

1. f, 1 Samuel 11:15
2. d, 1 Chronicles 15:29
3. e, Ezra 1:1–2
4. h, Esther 2:16–17
5. a, Isaiah 6:1
6. i, Daniel 3:19–30
7. b, Daniel 6:1, 16
8. j, Matthew 2:1
9. g, Acts 25:13, 24
10. c, Revelation 19:16

Letters

There is a great deal of correspondence mentioned in the Bible. Can you identify the author of each of the letters referred to below?

1. _____ sent letters to Ephraim and Manasseh to come to Jerusalem for the Passover.
2. _____ asked for a letter from King Artaxerxes to present to Asaph (the keeper of the king's forest) as he returned to rebuild Judah.
3. _____ wrote a letter supporting Mordecai's inauguration of the Feast of Purim.
4. _____ sent a letter to Joab to assign Uriah to the forefront of battle, and then withdraw from him.
5. _____ wrote a letter to King Darius when he found Jews rebuilding the ruins of Judah.
6. _____ wrote letters in King Ahab's name, as part of a scheme to get Naboth's vineyard.
7. _____ sent a letter to all the people Nebuchadnezzar had carried away captive from Jerusalem to Babylon.
8. _____ sought letters from the high priest to go to the synagogues in Damascus and seek out those who belonged to "the Way."
9. _____ wrote a letter to Philemon about his slave Onesimus.

Answers

1. Hezekiah, 2 Chronicles 30:1
2. Nehemiah, Nehemiah 2:7–8
3. Esther, Esther 9:20, 29
4. David, 2 Samuel 11:14–15
5. Tattenai, Ezra 5:6
6. Jezebel, 1 Kings 21:8–10
7. Jeremiah, Jeremiah 29:1
8. Saul (Paul), Acts 9:2
9. Paul, Philemon 19

The Long and Short of It

We have a saying, "Well, that's the long and the short of it."
Can you identify the *long* and *short* of things in the following
verses?

1. The Lord said to Moses, "Is the Lord's _____ shortened?"
2. Zophar said to Job, "The _____ of the wicked is short."
3. Isaiah says, "The _____ is too short to stretch oneself on it."
4. Paul says, "All have _____ and fall short of the glory of God."
5. Paul tells the Corinthians, "The _____ time has grown very short."
6. The Lord said to Joshua, "When they make a long blast with the _____ _____, . . . all the people shall shout."
7. The Lord was pleased with Solomon because "you have not asked for yourself long _____ or riches or the life of your enemies."
8. Jesus objected to scribes "who like to go about in long _____ . . . and for a pretense make long _____."
9. In the parable of the unjust judge, Jesus said, "And will not God vindicate his _____, who cry to him day and night?"

Answers

1. hand, Numbers 11:23
2. exulting, Job 20:5
3. bed, Isaiah 28:20
4. sinned, Romans 3:23
5. appointed, 1 Corinthians 7:29
6. ram's horn, Joshua 6:5
7. life, 1 Kings 3:11
8. robes/prayers, Mark 12:38–40
9. elect, Luke 18:7

Marriage

Monogamous marriage between the sexes is highly esteemed in the Christian tradition. Here are some verses about marriage. Can you supply the missing word (s)?

1. "There was a marriage at _____ in Galilee. . . ."
2. Jesus said, "A man shall . . . be joined to his wife, and the two shall be one _____."
3. Jesus warned, "What therefore God has joined together, let not man put _____."
4. Paul advised the Corinthians: "It is better to marry than to _____."
5. Paul argued that "the unbelieving husband is _____ through his wife, and the unbelieving wife is _____ through her husband."
6. "Let marriage be held in _____ among all."
7. "The husband should give to his wife her _____ _____, and likewise the wife to her husband."
8. "The wife should not _____ from her husband . . . the husband should not _____ his wife."
9. "In the _____ they neither marry nor are given in marriage. . . ."
10. "Blessed are those who are invited to the marriage _____ of the Lamb."

Answers

1. Cana, John 2:1
2. flesh, Matthew 19:5
3. asunder, Matthew 19:6
4. burn, 1 Corinthians 7:9, KJV
5. consecrated, 1 Corinthians 7:14
6. honor, Hebrews 13:4
7. conjugal rights, 1 Corinthians 7:3
8. separate/divorce, 1 Corinthians 7:10–11
9. resurrection, Matthew 22:30
10. supper, Revelation 19:9

32

Mathematics

Here are some statements that deal with mathematics—addition, subtraction, multiplication, and division. Can you supply the missing word?

1. "Make every effort to add to your faith _____."
2. "Why then the law? It was added because of _____."
3. (God) "multiplies my _____ without cause," said Job.
4. "Cast me not away from thy presence and take not thy _____ _____ from me."
5. "I will see you again . . . and no one will take your _____ from you."
6. "No _____ or _____ divided against itself will stand."
7. "Is _____ divided?"
8. "Those who choose another god multiply their _____."
9. "The Lord added to their _____ day by day those who were being saved."
10. "If _____ casts out _____, he is divided against himself."

Answers

1. goodness, 2 Peter 1:5, NIV
2. transgressions, Galatians 3:19
3. wounds, Job 9:17
4. holy spirit, Psalm 51:11
5. joy, John 16:22
6. city/house, Matthew 12:25
7. Christ, 1 Corinthians 1:13
8. sorrows, Psalm 16:4
9. number, Acts 2:47
10. Satan, Matthew 12:26

Moses

How well do you remember Old Testament stories? Try this quiz on the life of Moses, the prophet and lawgiver.

1. His father's name was _____.
2. His mother's name was _____.
3. He had a brother named _____, and a sister _____.
4. His wife's name was _____.
5. As an infant, he was rescued from death by _____ daughter.
6. He saw a _____ that was on fire, but not consumed.
7. Under God, he led his people out of their bondage to the rulers of _____.
8. He received the law from God on Mt. _____.
9. He led the people through the wilderness to the land of _____.
10. He was buried in a valley in the land of _____.

Answers

1. Amram, Exodus 6:20
2. Jochebed, Exodus 6:20
3. Aaron/Miriam, Exodus 6:20; 15:20
4. Zipporah, Exodus 2:21
5. Pharaoh's, Exodus 2:5

6. bush, Exodus 3:2
7. Egypt, Exodus 6:11
8. Sinai, Exodus 19:20
9. Canaan, Numbers 34:1
10. Moab, Deuteronomy 34:5, 6

They Were Murdered

God's command is "Thou shalt not kill" (Exod. 20:13), but murders are recorded in the Bible. Some who killed others were eventually redeemed. The verses below allude to some infamous murders. Can you identify the victim and the perpetrator(s)?

1. "Then they cast him out of the city and stoned him [to death]."
2. "You have smitten _____ the Hittite with the sword."
3. "_____ rose up against his brother _____, and killed him."
4. "He [_____] looked this way and that, and seeing no one he killed the Egyptian."
5. "_____, the wife of Heber took a tent peg . . . and drove the peg into his temple."
6. Then they went to _____, saying, '_____ has been stoned; he is dead.'"
7. "Give me at once the head of _____ on a platter."

Answers (Victim/Perpetrator[s])

1. Stephen/Sanhedrin, Acts 7:58
2. Uriah/David, 2 Samuel 12:9
3. Abel/Cain, Genesis 4:8
4. Egyptian/Moses, Exodus 2:12
5. Sisera/Jael, Judges 4:21
6. Jezebel/Naboth, 1 Kings 21:14
7. John the Baptist/Herod (Herodias, Salome), Mark 6:25

35

Nationalities

People of various nationalities are part of the biblical story. Some figure prominently, others play a minor role. Can you match the people on the left with their nationalities on the right?

1. Naaman	a. Arabian
2. Queen Candace	b. Egyptian
3. Sennacherib	c. Ethiopian
4. Artaxerxes	d. Roman
5. Geshem	e. Syrian
6. Nebuchadnezzar	f. Babylonian
7. Potiphar	g. Cyrenian
8. Claudius Lysias	h. Persian
9. Simon	i. Assyrian
10. Zipporah	j. Midianite

Answers

1. e, 2 Kings 5:1
2. c, Acts 8:27
3. i, 2 Kings 18:13
4. h, Ezra 4:7
5. a, Nehemiah 2:19

6. f, Daniel 1:1
7. b, Genesis 37:36
8. d, Acts 23:26
9. g, Matthew 27:32
10. j, Exodus 2:15–22

What's New?

Here are some biblical verses about newness (for the New Year). Can you tell "what's new" by filling in the missing word?

1. "A new _____ I give to you," said Jesus.
2. "And I [John] saw the . . . new _____, coming down from God out of heaven, prepared as a bride adorned for her husband."
3. "A new _____ I will give you, and a new _____ I will put within you," says God.
4. Lamentations notes: "They [Lord's mercies] are new every _____."
5. "They are filled with new _____," said skeptics at Pentecost.
6. The Ephesians were advised to "put on the new _____."
7. "As Christ was raised from the dead . . . we too might walk in newness of _____," Paul urges in Romans.
8. Paul said, "If any one is in Christ, he [or she] is a new _____."
9. "Behold, I make _____ _____ new," says God.
10. "Until that day when I _____ it new with you in my Father's kingdom."

Answers

1. commandment, John 13:34
2. Jerusalem, Revelation 21:2
3. heart/spirit, Ezekiel 36:26
4. morning, Lamentations 3:23
5. wine, Acts 2:13
6. nature, Ephesians 4:24
7. life, Romans 6:4
8. creation, 2 Corinthians 5:17
9. all things, Revelation 21:5
10. drink, Matthew 26:29

Noah

We are all familiar with the story of Noah and the ark. Supply the missing words below to show how well you remember the details of the story.

1. His grandfather, _____, is known as the oldest man in the Bible.
2. He had three sons: _____, _____, and _____.
3. God told him to make an ark of _____ wood.
4. He was to take _____ pairs of "clean" animals.
5. He was to take _____ pair of "unclean" animals.
6. God said it would rain for _____ days and _____ nights.
7. Noah was _____ _____ years old at the time of the flood.
8. When the flood abated, the ark rested on the mountains of _____.
9. The first bird Noah sent forth was a _____.
10. The bird he sent forth twice was a _____.
11. After the ark was empty, Noah's first act was to build an _____.
12. The sign of God's covenant with Noah was a _____.

Answers

1. Methuselah, Genesis 5:27
2. Shem/Ham/Japheth, Genesis 6:10
3. gopher, Genesis 6:14
4. seven, Genesis 7:2
5. one, Genesis 7:2
6. forty, Genesis 7:4
7. six hundred, Genesis 7:6
8. Ararat, Genesis 8:4
9. raven, Genesis 8:7
10. dove, Genesis 8:8
11. altar, Genesis 8:20
12. rainbow, Genesis 9:13, NIV

What Is It?

In the verses given or alluded to below, can you identify the missing object by filling in the word?

1. At Cana, Jesus used six stone _____ in performing his miracle.
2. The psalmist said, "Let their own _____ before them become a snare."
3. Isaiah complained, "The _____ is too short to stretch oneself on it."
4. Paul escaped the governor of Damascus with the help of a _____.
5. Nazarites took a vow that they would not use a _____.
6. Jesus charged his disciples to "take nothing for their journey except a _____" with them.
7. At the burning bush, God told Moses to remove his _____.
8. Jesus was anointed with oil from an alabaster _____.
9. Jesus criticized those who "make their _____ broad and their fringes long."
10. Abraham's servant (when seeking a wife for his son, Isaac) gave gifts to Rebekah: a gold ring and two _____.

Answers

1. jars, John 2:6
2. table, Psalm 69:22
3. bed, Isaiah 28:20
4. basket, 2 Corinthians 11:33
5. razor, Numbers 6:5
6. staff, Mark 6:8
7. shoes, Exodus 3:5
8. flask, Matthew 26:7; Mark 14:3
9. phylacteries, Matthew 23:5
10. bracelets, Genesis 24:22, 30

Occupations

Many occupations are listed in the Bible. Can you identify the work performed by the following people by supplying the missing word(s)?

1. Julius, who befriended Paul, was a _____.
2. Alexander, who did Paul "much evil," was a _____.
3. Felix, before whom Paul was tried, was a _____.
4. Paul asked Timothy to help Zenas the _____ with his trip.
5. Paul's convert, Sergius Paulus, was a _____.
6. Zacchaeus, with whom Jesus dined, was a _____.
7. Crispus, chief _____ of a synagogue, was a convert of Paul's.
8. Tertullus, who informed against Paul, was an _____.
9. Agrippa, whom Paul almost persuaded to be a Christian, was a _____.
10. Ananias, who informed against Paul, was a _____ _____.

Answers

1. centurion, Acts 27:1–3
2. coppersmith, 2 Timothy 4:14
3. governor, Acts 23:26
4. lawyer, Titus 3:12
5. proconsul, Acts 13:7
6. publican, Luke 19:2, KJV
7. ruler, Acts 18:8
8. orator, Acts 24:1
9. king, Acts 26:27
10. high priest, Acts 24:1

Paintings

The Bible has been an inspiration to many artists who have chosen biblical scenes as the subject for their paintings. Can you match artist and painting in the lists given below? Take extra credit if you can also identify the verse or passage that served as inspiration.

1. El Greco
2. Tintoretto
3. Salvador Dali
4. Sir Edward Burne-Jones
5. Fritz Von Uhde
6. Andrea Del Sarto
7. Heinrich Hofmann
8. Carlo Maratta
9. Eugene Burnend
10. Peter Paul Rubens

a. The Morning of the Resurrection
b. Suffer the Little Children
c. Christ and the Doctors (the Temple)
d. Peter and John (running)
e. Pentecost, The Descent of the Holy Spirit
f. Descent from the Cross
g. Christ of St. John of the Cross
h. John the Baptist
i. Christ at the Sea of Galilee
j. Holy Night

Answers

1. e, Acts 2
2. i, John 21:1–24
3. g, Matthew 27:35
4. a, John 20:1–18
5. b, Matthew 19:13–15
6. h, Luke 1:57–80
7. c, Luke 2:46–47
8. j, Luke 2:19
9. d, John 20:4
10. f, Matthew 27:58–60

Paintings (2)

The Bible has been an inspiration to many artists who have chosen biblical scenes as the subject for their paintings. Can you match artist and painting in the lists given below? Take extra credit if you can also identify the verse or passage that served as the inspiration.

1. Alfred Soord
2. Michelangelo Buonarroti
3. Raffaello Raphael
4. Angelo di Bondone (Gitto)
5. Leonardo Da Vinci
6. Jean-Francois Millet
7. William Holman Hunt
8. Mihaly Munkascy
9. Antonio Allegri da Correggio
10. Heinrich Hofmann

a. Christ Before Pilate
b. The Lost Sheep
c. The Last Supper
d. Christ in Gethsemane
e. The Last Judgment
f. The Nativity
g. Baptism of Christ
h. Miraculous Draught of Fish
i. Light of the World
j. The Sower

Answers

1. b, Luke 15:3–7
2. e, Matthew 25:31–46
3. h, Luke 5:1–11
4. g, Matthew 3:13–17
5. c, Matthew 26:17–30
6. j, Matthew 13:1–23
7. i, John 8:12; Revelation 3:20
8. a, Matthew 27:11–14
9. f, Luke 2:15
10. d, Matthew 26:39

Parables of Jesus

Jesus is known for his many parables, which have been defined as "earthly stories with heavenly meanings." The parable was his way of instructing us in spiritual truth. Supply the missing word in the following classic titles of the parables.

1. The New Wine and Old _____
2. The Wise and Foolish _____
3. The Children at _____
4. The Empty _____
5. The Uncompleted _____
6. The King's Rash _____
7. The Unmerciful _____
8. The Barren _____ _____
9. The Laborers and the _____
10. The Prodigal _____ and the Elder _____

Answers

1. Wineskins, Matthew 9:17
2. Builders, Matthew 7:24–27
3. Play, Matthew 11:16–19
4. House, Matthew 12:43–45
5. Tower, Luke 14:25–30
6. Warfare, Luke 14:31–33
7. Servant, Matthew 18:21–35
8. Fig Tree, Luke 13:6–9
9. Hours, Matthew 20:1–16
10. Son/Brother, Luke 15:11–32

Paradoxes

Perhaps, as you've read the Bible, you've felt the pull of opposites that nevertheless seem (paradoxically) to belong together to form a larger truth. Can you identify the opposites found in the following familiar verses of Scripture?

1. "The _____ of God is _____ than men."
2. "Where_____ abounded,_____ did abound more exceedingly."
3. "Behold then the _____ and _____ of God."
4. "For when I am _____, then am I _____."
5. "I know how to be _____, and I know also how to _____."
6. "In the world you have _____, but be of good _____."
7. "Be as wise as _____, and harmless as _____."
8. "The chastisement of our peace was upon him, and with his _____ we are _____."
9. "For your sake he became _____, that you through his _____ might be _____."
10. "As having _____, and yet possessing _____ _____."

Answers

1. weakness/stronger, 1 Corinthians 1:25
2. sin/grace, Romans 5:20
3. goodness/severity, Romans 11:22
4. weak/strong, 2 Corinthians 12:10
5. abased/abound, Philippians 4:12
6. tribulation/cheer, John 16:33
7. serpents/doves, Matthew 10:16
8. stripes/healed, Isaiah 53:5
9. poor/poverty/rich, 2 Corinthians 8:9
10. nothing/all things, 2 Corinthians 6:10

Poem Titles

Some of the greatest poems in the English language have been inspired by Scripture. The poet has selected a biblical personality or theme for his or her work. Can you match author and title in the lists given below? Take extra credit if you can identify the biblical book or verse involved.

1. William Blake	a. Hound of Heaven, The
2. Elizabeth Barrett Browning	b. I Am the Way
	c. Joy and Peace in Believing
3. Robert Browning	
4. William Cowper	d. Journey of the Magi, The
5. T. S. Eliot	
6. Alice Meynell	e. Lowest Place, The
7. John Milton	f. Mediator, The
8. John Henry Newman	g. New Jerusalem, The
9. Christina Rossetti	h. Pillar of the Cloud, The
10. Francis Thompson	i. Samson Agonistes
	j. Saul

Answers

1. g, Revelation 21:2
2. f, 1 Timothy 2:5
3. j, 1 Samuel 13–20
4. c, Romans 15:13
5. d, Matthew 2:7–12
6. b, John 14:6
7. i, Judges 13–17
8. h, Exodus 13:21; 33:9; Psalm 99:7
9. e, Luke 14:8–10
10. a, Job 7:21; Luke 19:10

Create a Portrait

If you were painting a detailed portrait of a person, you would need to include nearly all of the features to be found in the missing word(s) below (with the possible exception of #8). What are these features?

1. "Moses wist not that the _____ of his _____ shone."
2. "Keep me as the apple of the _____."
3. "The _____ of the wise seeks knowledge."
4. "_____ have they, but they _____ not."
5. "Set a watch, O LORD, before my _____."
6. "Cut off your _____ and cast it away. . ."
7. "Thou anointest my _____ with oil."
8. "Like vinegar to the _____ . . . so is the sluggard to those who send him."
9. "I became to them as one who eases the yoke on their _____."
10. "His name shall be on their _____."

Answers

1. skin/face, Exodus 34:29, KJV
2. eye, Psalm 17:8
3. ear, Proverbs 18:15
4. noses/smell, Psalm 115:6, KJV
5. mouth, Psalm 141:3, KJV
6. hair, Jeremiah 7:29
7. head, Psalm 23:5
8. teeth, Proverbs 10:26
9. jaws, Hosea 11:4
10. foreheads, Revelation 22:4

46

Public Prayers

Prayer in the Bible is both personal and corporate. According to scholars the portions of Scripture quoted below were originally public prayers or were later used as liturgical prayers. Can you identify the people who offered them?

1. "Alas, O Lord GOD, why hast thou brought this people over the Jordan at all . . . ."
2. "Thine, O LORD, is the greatness, and the power, and the glory, and the victory, and the majesty. . . ."
3. O LORD, God of Israel, there is no God like thee. . . ."
4. "Sovereign Lord, who didst make the heaven and the earth. . . ."
5. "Stand up and bless the LORD your God from everlasting to everlasting."
6. "Thou art the LORD, thou alone; thou hast made heaven. . . ."
7. "Thou art worthy to take the book. . . ."
8. "We give thee thanks, O Lord God Almighty. . . ."

Answers

1. Joshua, Joshua 7:7
2. David, 1 Chronicles 29:11
3. Solomon, 2 Chronicles 6:14
4. early church, Acts 4:24
5. Levites, Nehemiah 9:5
6. Ezra, Nehemiah 9:6–38
7. beasts and elders, Revelation 5:9, KJV
8. elders, Revelation 11:17, KJV

47

The Prophets

Some facts about the prophets are fairly well known. Can you identify the prophets, using the hints furnished in the left-hand column?

1. He learned God's love in his marriage.
2. He saw seraphim, and God high and lifted up.
3. He answered, "What does the Lord require of you?"
4. He stationed himself on a tower.
5. He had a scribe named Baruch.
6. He spoke of Nineveh's ruin.
7. He saw a valley of dry bones.
8. He saw a plague of locusts.
9. He saw God's Messenger, "like a refiner's fire."
10. This prophet wanted justice to flow.

a. Habakkuk
b. Ezekiel
c. Joel
d. Nahum
e. Jeremiah
f. Isaiah
g. Hosea
h. Malachi
i. Amos
j. Micah

Answers

1. g
2. f
3. j
4. a
5. e
6. d
7. b
8. c
9. h
10. i

Proverbial Sayings of Jesus

Many proverbial sayings of Jesus have passed into our common language. Can you distinguish his sayings from other proverbial sayings, and identify the source of each?

1. "Salt of the earth."
2. "Do not let your left hand know what your right hand is doing."
3. "Time eases all things."
4. "Eleventh hour."
5. "Better late than never."
6. Wolves in sheep's clothing.
7. "What's past is prologue."
8. "It is more blessed to give than to receive."
9. "Blind leaders of the blind."
10. "One swallow does not a summer make."

Answers

1. Jesus, Matthew 5:13
2. Jesus, Matthew 6:3
3. Sophocles, *Oedipus Rex,* lb.1.1515
4. Jesus, Matthew 20:6
5. Livy, *History,* lb. bk. IV, sec. 23
6. Jesus, Matthew 7:15
7. Shakespeare, *Tempest,* II, i, 257
8. Jesus, Acts 20:35
9. Jesus, Matthew 15:14
10. Aristotle, *Ethics,* lb.7

Proverbial Sayings in the Old Testament

Many proverbial sayings in the Old Testament have passed into our common language. Can you distinguish these sayings from other proverbial sayings, and identify the source of each one?

1. "God save the king."
2. "A man after his own heart."
3. "Possess your soul with patience."
4. "Set thine house in order."
5. "He that lies with the dogs, riseth with fleas."
6. "Man proposes, but God disposes."
7. "Lick the dust."
8. "We spend our years as a tale that is told."
9. "By hook or by crook."
10. "A soft answer turneth away wrath."

Answers

1. 1 Samuel 10:24
2. 1 Samuel 13:14
3. Dryden, *The Hind and the Panther*, lb.1.37
4. 2 Kings 20:1
5. George Herbert, *Jacula Prudentum*, lb.343
6. Thomas á Kempis, *Imitation*, lb.1919
7. Psalm 72:9
8. Psalm 90:9
9. John Wycliffe, *Tracts*
10. Proverbs 15:1

Proverbial Sayings of Paul

Many proverbial sayings of the apostle Paul have passed into our common language. Can you distinguish these sayings from other proverbial sayings, and identify the sources of each?

1. "Practice . . . what you preach."
2. "All things to all men."
3. "Moderation in all things."
4. "Heap coals of fire on his head."
5. "A thorn in the flesh."
6. "The wages of sin is death."
7. "While there's life, there's hope."
8. "Given to hospitality."
9. "The die is cast."
10. "Labor of love."

Answers

1. Plautus, *Asinaria,* act III, sc. iii, 1.644
2. Paul, 1 Corinthians 9:22
3. Terence, *Andria,* 1.61
4. Paul, Romans 12:20
5. Paul, 2 Corinthians 12:7
6. Paul, Romans 6:23
7. Cicero, *Ad Atticum,* lb. IX, 10
8. Paul, Romans 12:13
9. Julius Caesar, *Plutarch,* lb.32
10. Paul, 1 Thessalonians 1:3

51

Proverbial Sayings in the Prophets

Many proverbial sayings in the prophets have passed into our common language. Can you distinguish these sayings from other proverbial sayings, and identify the sources of each one?

1. "Absence makes the heart grow fonder."
2. "The fathers have eaten a sour grape, and the children's teeth are set on edge."
3. "According to the law of the Medes and the Persians, which altereth not."
4. "Haste maketh waste."
5. "They have sown the wind, and they shall reap the whirlwind."
6. "Can we ever have too much of a good thing?"
7. "Can two walk together, except they be agreed?"
8. "Put your shoulder to the wheel."
9. "Write the vision, and make it plain upon tables, that he may run that readeth it."
10. "The life which is unexamined is not worth living."

Answers

1. Sextus Propertius, *Elegies,* lb. xxxiii, 43
2. Jeremiah 31:29
3. Daniel 6:12
4. John Heywood, *Proverbs,* pt. I, ch. 2
5. Hosea 8:7
6. Cervantes, *Don Quixote,* I, 6, p. 37
7. Amos 3:3
8. Aesop, *Hercules and the Wagoner*
9. Habakkuk 2:2
10. Plato, *Apology*

52

Questions Jesus Asked

Jesus often asked his listeners questions, for he knew that questions are marvelous teachers. Can you complete the questions he asked in the sampling of verses below?

1. "Why are you _____, O men of little faith?"
2. "Are not two _____ sold for a penny?"
3. "Have you not read what _____ did, when he was hungry . . . ?"
4. "And if I cast out demons by _____, by whom do your sons cast them out?"
5. "He said to them, 'But who do you say that _____ _____ ?'"
6. "Why do you see the _____ that is in your brother's eye, but do not notice the _____ that is in your own eye?"
7. "And Jesus said to him, 'Why do you call me _____ ?'"
8. "Which of these three, do you think, proved _____ . . . ?"
9. "Which of you by being _____ can add a cubit to his span of life?"
10. "For which of you, desiring to build a _____, does not first sit down and count the cost, whether he has enough to complete it?"

Answers

1. afraid, Matthew 8:26
2. sparrows, Matthew 10:29
3. David, Matthew 12:3–4
4. Beelzebul, Matthew 12:27
5. I am, Matthew 16:15
6. speck/log, Matthew 7:3
7. good, Luke 18:19
8. neighbor, Luke 10:36
9. anxious, Luke 12:25
10. tower, Luke 14:28

Second Place

It is always a little harder to be in second place, or to remember who is in second place. Can you remember?

1. Joseph's second dream was about _____.
2. The second lot for Canaan's land went to _____.
3. Solomon began building the temple in the second month, _____.
4. The second face in Ezekiel's vision was that of a _____.
5. The second beast in Daniel's vision was like a _____.
6. The second chariot in Zechariah's vision had black _____.
7. _____ inquired of Jesus about a second birth.
8. _____ are second in Paul's list of church leaders.
9. Paul says, "The second man is the _____."
10. Those who conquer won't be hurt by "the second _____."

Answers

1. grain, Genesis 41:5
2. Simeon, Joshua 19:1
3. Ziv, 1 Kings 6:1
4. man, Ezekiel 10:14
5. bear, Daniel 7:5
6. horses, Zechariah 6:2
7. Nicodemus, John 3:4
8. prophets, 1 Corinthians 12:28
9. Lord, 1 Corinthians 15:47, KJV
10. death, Revelation 2:11

Simon Says:
But Which Simon?

There are a number of people in the Bible who have the name of Simon. Can you distinguish one from another by using the clues given below?

1. How was this Simon related to Jesus?
2. This Simon (an apostle) was identified as a member of which Jewish patriotic party?
3. What new name did Jesus give this Simon (who was also an apostle)?
4. This Simon (in whose home a sinful woman anointed Jesus' feet) belonged to which Jewish religious "party"?
5. What serious disease did this Simon (who lived in Bethany) have?
6. This Simon carried Jesus' cross. From what city did he hail?
7. In what way did this Simon (Magus) earn his living?
8. How did this Simon (who lived at Joppa) earn his living?
9. This Simon has the misfortune of being remembered for the deed of which infamous son?

Answers

1. brother, Matthew 13:55
2. the Zealot, Luke 6:15
3. Peter, Matthew 10:2; 16:13–18
4. Pharisee, Luke 7:36–50
5. leprosy, Matthew 26:6; Mark 14:3
6. Cyrene, Matthew 27:32; Mark 15:21
7. magic, Acts 8:9
8. tanner, Acts 9:43
9. Judas Iscariot, John 6:71

Under Our Skin

The psalmist says, "I am fearfully and wonderfully made" (Ps. 139:14). And we are remarkable creatures, inside and out. Can you identify the things that are "under our skin" by supplying the missing word(s) below?

1. God used a _____ from Adam in creating Eve.
2. The "man" Jacob wrestled touched the _____ of his thigh.
3. Job said that if he ever lifted a hand against the father-less, "then let my _____ _____ fall from my shoulder."
4. The king of Babylon engaged in divination by looking at a _____.
5. Ezekiel was to say, "O dry _____, hear the word of the LORD."
6. Isaiah saw the sword of the Lord filled with . . . "the fat of the _____ of rams."
7. "Blessed are the pure in _____: for they shall see God."
8. When he confessed Jesus as the Christ, Jesus told Peter that "flesh and _____" had not revealed this to him.
9. Jesus was crucified at Golgotha, known also as "a place of a _____."
10. Timothy was advised to sip some wine "for the sake of your _____ and your frequent ailments."

Answers

1. rib, Genesis 2:21–22
2. sinew, Genesis 32:32
3. shoulder blade, Job 31:22
4. liver, Ezekiel 21:21
5. bones, Ezekiel 37:4
6. kidneys, Isaiah 34:6
7. heart, Matthew 5:8
8. blood, Matthew 16:17
9. skull, Matthew 27:33
10. stomach, 1 Timothy 5:23

Precious Stones

A number of jewels and precious stones are mentioned in the Bible. Can you identify them by supplying the missing word in the following quotations or descriptions?

1. "The price of [wisdom] is above _____."
2. Isaiah sees God restoring Israel like a restored city, making "windows of _____."
3. In that same vision, Isaiah sees "gates of _____."
4. Jeremiah notes that "the sin of Judah is written with a pen of iron, and with the point of a _____."
5. The wheels in Ezekiel's vision were of the color of a _____ stone.
6. Jesus said, "The kingdom of heaven is like a merchant in search of fine _____."
7. In the Book of Revelation, John sees horses with "breastplates of fire, and of _____."
8. In the Book of Revelation, John sees "one" sitting on a throne encircled by what looked like an _____ rainbow.
9. In the Book of Revelation, the light of the heavenly city was like a _____ stone.

Answers

1. rubies, Job 28:18, KJV
2. agates, Isaiah 54:12
3. carbuncles, Isaiah 54:12
4. diamond, Jeremiah 17:1
5. chrysolite, Ezekiel 1:16; 10:9
6. pearls, Matthew 13:45
7. jacinth (sapphire), Revelation 9:17
8. emerald, Revelation 4:2–3
9. jasper, Revelation 21:10–11

Titles Ascribed to God

Supply the missing words in the verses given below (from the King James Version), and reflect on a few of the many titles ascribed to God.

1. "He that dwelleth in the secret place of the most High shall abide under the shadow of the _____."
2. "Lord, shew us the _____, and it sufficeth us."
3. "Thus saith the high and lofty one that inhabiteth eternity, whose name is _____."
4. "Now unto the _____ eternal, immortal, invisible, the only wise God, be honor and glory for ever and ever."
5. "Shall not the _____ of all the earth do right?"
6. "The eternal God is thy _____."
7. "Let us make a joyful noise to the _____ of our salvation."
8. "The LORD is my _____, I shall not want."
9. "This is his name whereby he shall be called, THE LORD OUR _____."
10. "My spirit hath rejoiced in God my _____."

Answers

1. Almighty, Psalm 91:1
2. Father, John 14:8
3. Holy, Isaiah 57:15
4. King, 1 Timothy 1:17
5. Judge, Genesis 18:25
6. refuge, Deuteronomy 33:27
7. rock, Psalm 95:1
8. shepherd, Psalm 23:1
9. RIGHTEOUSNESS, Jeremiah 23:6
10. Savior, Luke 1:47

The Titles of Jesus

Supply the missing words in the verses given below, and reflect on a few of the many titles that have been ascribed to Jesus, the Christ.

1. "Behold the _____ of God, who takes away the sin of the world."
2. "Christ our _____ is sacrificed for us."
3. "To _____ our feet into the way of peace."
4. "A _____ of publicans and sinners."
5. "I have given you an _____."
6. "God exalted him with his right hand to be a Prince and a _____."
7. "But if any one does sin, we have an _____ with the Father."
8. "We know thou art a _____ come from God."
9. (Christ Jesus) "emptied himself, taking the form of a _____."
10. "And every tongue confess that Jesus Christ is _____."

Answers

1. Lamb, John 1:29
2. passover, 1 Corinthians 5:7
3. guide, Luke 1:79
4. friend, Luke 7:34, KJV
5. example, John 13:15
6. Savior, Acts 5:31
7. advocate, 1 John 2:1
8. teacher, John 3:2
9. servant, Philippians 2:7
10. Lord, Philippians 2:11

Tools of the Trade

The Jews of biblical times held manual labor in high regard, believing all men should have a craft or trade. Jesus was a carpenter. Paul was a tentmaker. Can you identify the tools used by various workers by supplying the missing word?

1. The Lord asked Job, "Can you draw out leviathan with a _____?"
2. Isaiah saw nations beating their "swords into _____."
3. Isaiah also saw them beating their "spears into _____."
4. Isaiah saw every one helping his neighbor, "he who smooths with the hammer him who strikes the _____. . . ."
5. Isaiah saw a seraphim "having in his hand a burning coal which he had taken with _____ from the altar."
6. The Lord said to Jeremiah, "Is not my word like . . . a _____ which breaks the rock in pieces?"
7. The Lord also said to Jeremiah, "The _____ blow fiercely, the lead is consumed by the fire. . . ."
8. Amos saw the Lord "standing . . . with a _____ in his hand."
9. John the Baptist said, "Even now the _____ is laid to the root of the trees."

Answers

1. fishhook, Job 41:1
2. plowshares, Isaiah 2:4
3. pruninghooks, Isaiah 2:4
4. anvil, Isaiah 41:7
5. tongs, Isaiah 6:6

6. hammer, Jeremiah 23:29
7. bellows, Jeremiah 6:29
8. plumbline, Amos 7:7
9. axe, Matthew 3:10

"Who Touched Me?"

Jesus asked, "Who touched me?" (Mark 5:31) He was often physically touched by people, and he touched them. Can you identify who Jesus touched or touched Jesus in the following descriptions?

1. Who was the girl he took by the hand, bidding her to rise?
2. He touched the fevered mother-in-law of which disciple?
3. He touched a boy suffering from which disease?
4. He touched (washed) the feet of the people in which group?
5. What problem did the woman have who touched his garment?
6. Whose ear did Jesus touch and heal?
7. Who did Jesus take in his arms and bless?
8. What other problem did the epileptic boy have?
9. What problem did the woman have on whom Jesus laid his hands?
10. Jesus touched these two men and cured which malady?

Answers

1. Jairus' daughter, Mark 5:22, 41
2. Peter, Matthew 8:14–15
3. epilepsy, Mark 9:27
4. disciples, John 13:5
5. bleeding, Mark 5:28–29, NIV
6. high priest's slave, John 18:10
7. children, Mark 10:15–16
8. deaf and dumb spirit, Mark 9:25–27
9. bent, crippled, Luke 13:11–13
10. blindness, Matthew 9:27–29

61

Christian Unity

Jesus prayed for his disciples that "they may all be one" (John 17:21). Christian unity is a significant theme throughout the New Testament and a continuing concern of contemporary Christians. Here are some verses about unity. Can you supply the missing word?

1. "The company of those who _____ were of one heart and soul . . . they had everything in common."
2. Endeavoring to keep the unity of the _____."
3. "[God] hath made of one _____ all nations of men. . . ."
4. "Be at _____ with one another."
5. "So there shall be one _____, one _____."
6. "Because there is one _____, we who are many are one body. . . ."
7. "For by one Spirit we were all _____ into one body. . . ."
8. "For you are all _____ in Christ Jesus."
9. "You are no longer strangers and sojourners, but you are _____ _____ with the saints, and members of the household of God."
10. "There is one body, and one Spirit, just as you were called to the one _____ that belongs to your call."

Answers

1. believed, Acts 4:32
2. Spirit, Ephesians 4:3, KJV
3. blood, Acts 17:26, KJV
4. peace, Mark 9:50
5. flock/shepherd, John 10:16
6. bread, 1 Corinthians 10:17
7. baptized, 1 Corinthians 12:13
8. one, Galatians 3:28
9. fellow citizens, Ephesians 2:19
10. hope, Ephesians 4:4

Household Utensils

The verses quoted or alluded to below mention a variety of common household utensils found in homes of biblical times. Can you identify them by supplying the missing word?

1. (Elisha) asked her, "What hast thou in the house? And she said, Thine handmaid hath not any thing in the house, save a _____ of oil."
2. (The children of Israel) "look to other gods, and love _____ of wine."
3. "Or ever the silver cord be loosed, or the golden _____ be broken."
4. "This _____ is the new testament in my blood."
5. "He that dippeth his hand with me in the _____, the same shall betray me."
6. (At Cana) "there were set there six _____ of stone."
7. "He poureth water into a _____, and began to wash the disciples' feet."
8. "Ye Pharisees make clean the outside of the cup and the _____. . . . ."
9. "New wine must be put into new _____; and both are preserved."
10. "Go into the city, and there shall meet you a man bearing a _____ of water."

Answers

1. pot, 2 Kings 4:2
2. flagons, Hosea 3:1
3. bowl, Ecclesiastes 12:6
4. cup, 1 Corinthians 11:25
5. dish, Matthew 26:23
6. waterpots, John 2:6
7. basin (bason, KJV), John 13:5
8. platter, Luke 11:39
9. bottles, Luke 5:38
10. pitcher, Mark 14:13

Valleys

Several Hebrew words are translated by the English word *valley.* So a valley can be as we know it, or a ravine or glen, or simply lowlands. Using the descriptive phrase in the left column, can you match it with the appropriate valley in the column to your right?

1. David battled Goliath in this valley.
2. Naboth's vineyard was in this valley.
3. Achan was punished for misdeeds in this valley.
4. The moon stood still in this valley.
5. This valley is made a place of springs.
6. King Josiah fought King Neco in this valley.
7. Samson's Delilah was from this valley.
8. Philistines occupied this valley against David.
9. Joel saw a judgment of nations in this valley.
10. Sodom and Gomorrah were located in this valley.

a. Ajalon
b. Siddim
c. Baca
d. Elah
e. Achor
f. Jehoshaphat
g. Sorek
h. Megiddo
i. Rephaim
j. Jezreel

Answers

1. d, 1 Samuel 17:19
2. j, Joshua 19:18
3. e, Joshua 7:24
4. a, Joshua 10:12
5. c, Psalm 84:6

6. h, 2 Chronicles 35:20–22
7. g, Judges 16:4
8. i, 2 Samuel 5:18
9. f, Joel 3:1–2
10. b, Genesis 14:3

You Have a Visitor

One of life's great delights is to be visited by someone you know and love. Many visits are recorded in Scripture. Can you name the people who speak about visits in the verses or descriptions given below?

1. _____ said, "I was sick and you visited me."
2. _____ said "pure religion" was "to visit orphans and widows."
3. _____ visited her "kinswoman" Elizabeth.
4. The _____ _____ _____ _____ "visited and redeemed his people."
5. _____ visited "his brethren" at age forty.
6. _____ wanted to visit every city where he had preached.
7. _____ _____ came "from the east" to visit a newborn king.
8. The _____ _____ said, "I will arise and go to my father. . . ."
9. _____ visited Jesus by night.
10. _____ said to his brothers, "I am about to die; but God will visit you. . . ."

Answers

1. Jesus, Matthew 25:36
2. James, James 1:27
3. Mary, Luke 1:39–40
4. Lord God of Israel, Luke 1:68
5. Moses, Acts 7:23
6. Paul, Acts 15:36
7. Wise Men, Matthew 2:1–12
8. Prodigal Son, Luke 15:18
9. Nicodemus, John 3:2
10. Joseph, Genesis 50:24

Where Do They Live?

"Homes" for some animals are natural habitats; some are man-made. Supply the missing words below to identify where the animals live.

1. Daniel was cast into a _____ of lions.
2. "The sparrow hath found an _____."
3. "And the swallow a _____ for herself."
4. A child will play on the _____ of an asp.
5. Saul pursued David in Engedi and "came to the _____ by the way."
6. God told Ezekiel he would make Rabbah a _____ for camels.
7. "As a _____ is full of birds, so are their houses full of deceit."
8. "Foxes have _____, and the birds of the air have nests."

Answers

1. den, Daniel 6:7
2. house, Psalm 84:3, KJV
3. nest, Psalm 84:3, KJV
4. hole, Isaiah 11:8

5. sheepcotes, 1 Samuel 24:3
6. stable, Ezekiel 25:5
7. cage, Jeremiah 5:27
8. holes, Matthew 8:20

God's Word

"Open my eyes, that I may behold wondrous things out of thy law," says the psalmist (Ps. 119:18). And his words are a prayer to use in the study of the Bible. Can you supply the missing word in these verses about God's Word?

1. "For the word of God is _____ and active, sharper than any two-edged sword."
2. Now the parable is this: "The _____ is the word of God."
3. "And take the helmet of salvation, and the _____ of the Spirit, which is the word of God."
4. "And have tasted the _____ of the word of God."
5. "Thy word is a _____ to my feet and a _____ to my path."
6. "Thy word is _____ from the beginning: and every one of thy righteous judgments endureth for ever."
7. "The word of the Lord is _____: he is a buckler to all them that trust in him."
8. "So shall my word be that goes forth from my mouth: it shall not return to me _____."
9. "_____ the Scriptures; because you think that in them you have eternal life: and it is they that bear witness to me."
10. "The grass withers, the flower fades, but the word of our God will _____ for ever."

Answers

1. living, Hebrews 4:12
2. seed, Luke 8:11
3. sword, Ephesians 6:17
4. goodness, Hebrews 6:5
5. lamp/light, Psalm 119:105
6. true, Psalm 119:160
7. tried, 2 Samuel 22:31
8. empty, Isaiah 55:11
9. search, John 5:39
10. stand, Isaiah 40:8